Rhyming Stars

Edited By Megan Roberts

First published in Great Britain in 2020 by:

Young Writers
Remus House
Coltsfoot Drive
Peterborough
PE2 9BF
Telephone: 01733 890066
Website: www.youngwriters.co.uk

Printed and bound in the UK by BookPrintingUK
Website: www.bookprintinguk.com
YB0432P

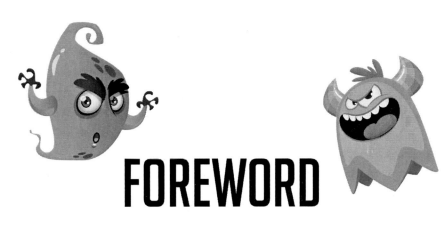

FOREWORD

Hello Reader!

For our latest poetry competition we sent out funky and vibrant worksheets for primary school pupils to fill in and create their very own poem about fiendish fiends and crazy creatures. I got to read them and guess what? They were **roarsome**!

The pupils were able to read our example poems and use the fun-filled free resources to help bring their imaginations to life, and the result is pages **oozing** with exciting poetic tales. From friendly monsters to mean monsters, from bumps in the night to **rip-roaring** adventures, these pupils have excelled themselves, and now have the joy of seeing their work in print!

Here at Young Writers we love nothing more than poetry and creativity. We aim to encourage children to put pen to paper to inspire a love of the written word and explore their own unique worlds of creativity. We'd like to congratulate all of the aspiring authors that have created this book of **monstrous mayhem** and we know that these poems will be enjoyed for years to come. So, dive on in and submerge yourself in all things furry and fearsome (and perhaps check under the bed!).

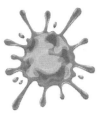

CONTENTS

Alfie Harris (8)	65	Taylin Large (8)	108
Vinny Gary Murray (8)	66	Mikah Demetrio Jay Richards (8)	109
Evie Bladd (8)	67	Poppie Grant-Richardson (7)	110
Christiana Stainton (9)	68	Lucas Wojtas (7)	111
Jamie-Lee Hlasi	69	Aimee W (8)	112
Isabelle Headland (8)	70	Honey Star Richmond-Turner (7)	113
Riley Cook (8)	71	Shayla Lucy Timms (7)	114
Avijit Tirumalasetti (7)	72	Jack Maxwell-Reeve (7)	115
Oliver Crisp (8)	73	Amelie Rose Liversidge (7)	116
William Jackson (7)	74	Ella Clayson (8)	117
Joshua Howes (7)	75	Anya Arbon	118
Noah Whitehouse (8)	76		

Haxby Road Primary School, York

Joseph Jackson (8)	119
Sahasra Thotakura (7)	120
Lois Rycroft (8)	121
Leo Wood (8)	122
Teagan Mia Smith (8)	123

Oliver O'Keeffe (8)	77
Archie Edwards (8)	78
Joel Osadi (8)	79
Nathaniel Korsah (7)	80
Tom Davison (7)	81
Charlie Scott (7)	82
Kea'Rae Caroline Quinlan (7)	83
Emily Thomas (8)	84
Harry Verschuren (7)	85
Lola Grace Rosenwink (8)	86
Niamh Cahill-Testouri (8)	87
Mikey Sapsford (7)	88
Jared Aitken (7)	89
Alfie James Newman (8)	90
Maya Wegner (7)	91
Jeremy Garcia (8)	92
Ozzy Chace Dyer (7)	93
Nana Adom Akyampong (7)	94
Amelie Morgan (8)	95
Lacey Lou Wales (8)	96
Harrison Brown (8)	97
Gracie-Mae Faulkner (7)	98
Bobby Johnson (7)	99
Phoebe Parker (7)	100
Bailey Ryan Carter (8)	101
Felicite Joy (7)	102
Bobby Moffat (8)	103
David Neagu (7)	104
Waleed Ahmad (7)	105
Eliza Jane Harrison (7)	106
Theo Barbet (7)	107

Onthank Primary School, Kilmarnock

Victoria McGinn (11)	124
Joe Henry Dudgeon (11)	125
Matthew O'Hare (11)	126
Neve Robertson (11)	127
Ellie Kerr (11)	128
Olivia Cooper (11)	129
Rhys Krupp (11)	130
Miller Davidson (11)	131
Tyler Qua (11)	132
Luke Fairbairn (10)	133
Phoebe Black (11)	134
Erin Mary Williams (10)	135
Christopher Brown (11)	136
Alex Chudleigh (11)	137
Jack Edgar (10)	138
Kyle Hamilton (11)	139
Kirsten Roberson (11)	140
Carly Inglis (11)	141
Morgan Clark (10)	142

Regis Manor Primary School, Milton Regis

Emmanuel Dumbuya (7)	143
Jessica Jane Carter (7)	144
Grace Charley-Beth Evans (7)	145
Tyler Bowyer (8)	146
Robert Daniel Holmes (8)	147
Rusne Erichova (7)	148
Erin Victoria Brown (7)	149
Irene Ojo-Igbinoba (7)	150
Autumn Stone (8)	151
Roseanna Heron (7)	152
Deivids Valdmanis (7)	153
Ellie Telfer (7)	154
Jack Hancock (8)	155
Madison Yuze Xue (7)	156
Maximus Tyler Drake Goodman (7)	157
Finley Sean Hooker (7)	158
Hayden John Pride (7), Kayden Barnes (7), Jai, Victor & Frankie	159
Ebony Rae Wood (7)	160
Dylan Dooley (7)	161
Holly Macey (7)	162
Ruby Milburn (7)	163
Max Shrubsall (8)	164

THE POEMS

Sweet Tooth Monster

There was a story, there was a tale
About the sweet-tooth monster who was sent in
the mail
One Saturday morning, early as could be
There was a bang at the door, what could it be?
I opened the door, it was a package for me
I opened the box to see what it could be
A sweet-tooth monster staring at me
Eight eyes so scary, nine sets of teeth
So sharp, but the smell of its breath was like
yummy jam tarts
His stay was short but still long enough for him
To fill my bedroom with yummy, sweet floof!

Ashton Brendan Eric Cockitt Hone (8)
Bradford Academy, Bradford

The Five Scary Monsters

There are five scary monsters sitting on the bed
The first one said, "Let's knock on someone's head."
The second one said, "Let's act scary."
The third one said, "Why are you so hairy?"
The fourth one said, "Heard a silly sound!"
The fifth one said, "There is no one else around."
And something fell on the ground
Then, *whoosh!* went the wind
And, "Eek!" someone said
So then the five scary monsters ran under the bed.

Ayesha Zaib (8)
Bradford Academy, Bradford

The Haunted Crow

Once there was a crow who could flow
He stood around the park with dogs that could bark
He roared at other people by moving his eyeballs
He was also made of feathers made of ultimate leather
He was that scary, he could make people scream
And that was his dream
He saw a beam of light with an aeroplane taking flight
Zoom! He shot up to the sky and into the plane
The passengers screamed like they were insane
Finally, his dream came true
This is what he wanted to do.

Rajab Suleman (8)
Bradford Academy, Bradford

Fun Party With Shape-Shifter

Shape-Shifter is a beast
And likes to have a savage feast

He likes to roam around
And change into different, funny things

Although he is friendly and nice
But some people are afraid and run like mice

Some people hang around and want to have a laugh
They try to tell others that Shape-Shifter is nice

Slowly, slowly, everyone gets to know
Shape-Shifter is nice and can join the party now.

Kasif Imran (9)
Bradford Academy, Bradford

Never Be Scared Or Lonely - Be Friendly

Damaggogan, the big, friendly foe
He is fearsome and handsome

Damaggogan, the big, friendly foe
He has a big nose to go with his big smile

Damaggogan, the big, friendly foe
He has magical powers and flies over towers of London

Damaggogan, the big, friendly foe
Has many faces and walks many places

Damaggogan banishes evil and protects good
Damaggogan, the big, friendly monster.

Amin Rashid (8)
Bradford Academy, Bradford

Spotty's Nemesis

Spotty Potty was a superhero who fought all the villains
He could hear for miles and miles away
And could fly anywhere he wanted to go
He fought villains all day, every day
He could not stop because there were so many villains
Eventually, he defeated them all so the next day
He went out to help the old lady cross the road safely
And he saw the principal's golden, colossal, gold mansion.

Junior Ingham (8)
Bradford Academy, Bradford

The Hobdy

Hobdy is not known yet
Although he has seven heads
He should wear a monster crown
Just for knocking buildings down
He's quite clever, very strong
Almost thirty centimetres long
When he moves, he likes to wiggle
Making other monsters giggle.

Adam Kucharski (7)
Bradford Academy, Bradford

Stiggy Is...

Stiggy is stinky
Stiggy is tall
Stiggy is intelligent
Stiggy is giggly
Stiggy is gross
Stiggy is yucky
But he can also be hungry

Stiggy comes to eat
Stiggy smells his feet
Stiggy likes to tweet
But he also likes sweets.

Laiba Hussain (8)
Bradford Academy, Bradford

Unknown Monster

Dark, windy, shadowy nights
Hairy, smelly legs with tights
Eyes full with blood
Feel like it was stuck in a flood
Disgusting smell is spreading
Just like rotten fish shredding
Run to save myself
Can't imagine I was itself.

Nimrah Ashraf (10)
Bradford Academy, Bradford

Gobler

My monster Gobler is the world's best wobbler
She wobbles all day, she wobbles all night
She even wobbles when she is in fright
I love her so much because she loves me too much
I love her cuddles because she's soft and she
wobbles.

Aliyah Akhtar (9)
Bradford Academy, Bradford

Loona The Lovely Monster

L ovely Loona sings all day

O h my, she loves to play

O n the climbing frame, on the swing

N ight and day, she will still sing

A round the apple tree, the bells will ring.

A'va Brown (8)

Bradford Academy, Bradford

My Monster

He may look cute, but honestly, he's horrifically
crazy, you do not want him.
He could cost you money that you don't have, you
do not want him.
He is a danger to you, you could end up homeless.
He'll steal your sweets, he'll empty your sugar pot.
He'll eat all the cookies in the night.
In the morning, he sleeps a while until you all leave
the room.
When you're not in the room, you'll hear bangs and
crashes,
Booms and smashes, you'll run upstairs
And he'll be asleep.
You do not want him.
But don't worry, he's only dangerous
If you're in the room.
You do not want him.
Don't keep trying to get rid of him, it is easier to
move house.
If you do, make sure he's not in the car,
because If he is, then you will just with live with the
horrors of Big, Blue Billy.

You do not want him.
Don't bother getting him to help.
He'll cause you to make an almighty yelp.
Be careful, he bites.
Trust me, you do not want him.

Jolyon George Tatam-Melia (10)
Colden Junior & Infant School, Colden

Big Toe

Big Toe creeping through the night
The tricky shape-shifter
Scary, scary
People run away
Hiding under beds
Making creepy noises
Roar
Big Toe screams
People get together
They make a plan
"Let's kill Big Toe,"
The people shout
Throwing spears and pitchforks
Flames, torches and burning paper balls
They chase Big Toe
They surround him
He's captured
There's nothing he can do

They kill him
They drag him
They all shout
"Good riddance monsters!"

Jack Simon (10)
Colden Junior & Infant School, Colden

The Acid Monster

Beware as there is something called an acid
monster
They're sneaky and they're sly
You'll hear them coming up your stairs
You may even cry
As your door creaks right open
You see a dark black shadow
As it makes its way towards you
A tingle could start in your toe
You close our eyes as you hide
Under the covers with fear
So you'd better watch out
Because they'll be near.

Rosie Dowson (11)
Colden Junior & Infant School, Colden

Beware The Living Teddy Bear

In the day, he's weak and mild
But at night, he's furious and wild

He jumps down the stairs
And swings from the light
To give everyone a sleepless night

He's got puppy eyes
But don't you see?
The devil inside
Is trying to get free

At daylight
He will look like he slept
But behind the disguise
Is a secret well-kept.

Lauren Yirrell (10)
Colden Junior & Infant School, Colden

Secrets

One turbulent night
Damp and sodden
A terrible fright
Is not forgotten
Climbing through the letterbox
Creeping up the stairs
Slyly sneaking like a fox
Into your nightmares
Sliding underneath the bed
A child jumps on and sits
Has the creature yet been fed?
No one knows, secrets are secrets...

Nicole Rodgers (9)
Colden Junior & Infant School, Colden

What It Has...

It has fangs
Sharp, bloody fangs
It has horns
Curly, spiky horns
It has wings
Scaly, smooth wings
It has a tail
A pointy, poisonous tail
It has an eye
A mischievous yellow eye
But...
It loves chicken!

Ella Clark (10)
Colden Junior & Infant School, Colden

Monsters Are Everywhere

M onsters are around you

O n the floor

N ever seeing anything

S till silent

T errified of death

E very living

R eally wrecking your house

S o annoyingly close.

Kaiden Smith (9)
Colden Junior & Infant School, Colden

Monster In My House

That laugh, I know too well
He's only there in the night
When he gets me, I'll go to Hell
He always causes quite a fright
He comes from the big hill
He's an old monster called Bill.

Rowan Sweeney (10)
Colden Junior & Infant School, Colden

YoungWriters
Est. 1991

My Monster, Scruffy

My best friend is a monster
He is not perfect because he is funny

His name is Scruffy
He has smooth, soft fur which is purple
With pink spots
He has yellow googly eyes and a long tongue
That smells of lavender
He wears a golden hat with a picture of a monster
On the front that squirts green ink
When he presses the eighth spot on his tummy

His favourite hobby is playing the blue guitar
He doesn't like it when the sky is gloomy
Because it makes him very moody
He likes to play smooth, calm music
In the dusky dawn

I amble to the bottom of my garden to pay a visit
His house is hidden by a rainbow of pretty white
lilies
I hear his tranquil songs mingled with the call
Of the birds and fluttering butterfly wings doing a
dance

I walk into Scruffy's house and look around
To see his littered home
Full of colourful berries

I give him a gift
A creamy, pink-looking baby toy llama
He is so cheerful to see me
And he appreciates his new toy.

Lili Marley (8)
Eveline Day School, Tooting

The Burger Monster

The little boy walking down the street,
He found something strange that he thought he
could eat,
There was a burger in the bushes!
But the Burger Monster opened its eyes,
"Argh!" screamed the little boy and everyone
heard his cries,
He called 999 and the surprised police whizzed out
of their cars,
Though all they could see was a burger in the
bushes,
The little boy told the police it was all a mistake!
But it happened again and again when the Burger
Monster opened his eyes,
The Burger Monster was so smart, he created a
potion of flying,
And that night, he sneaked into the house and flew
up the stairs,
He quietly crept into the little boy's room,
And sat in the corner in the light of the moon,
In the morning, the little boy woke with horror,
As the Burger Monster opened his eyes, what a
terror!

Thomas Smith (7)
Eveline Day School, Tooting

Watch Out For Gloopy!

Watch out for Gloopy
He can chop and gnash his teeth in children
He'll slither under the bed
For whatever it takes to grab little children
He will eat them for supper
He will bathe them in snot
And put salt and pepper on them
He will go to Pennsylvania at gone midnight
He will ninja-chop the lock
And creep up the stairs
And open your door
You'd better hide under your cover
Before he finds you under your bed
But some brave and fierce children
Tried to fight and battle with all their might
But Gloopy always won
But what Gloopy really wants
Is a friend to lie with.

Sofia Maryam Cooper (7)
Eveline Day School, Tooting

The Shadow Monster

Midnight, only a few chimes away
My room is as quiet as a mouse
My house is asleep

Tip! Tap! Tip! Tap!
What was that?
Tip! Tap! Tip! Tap!
There it was again

My door creaked open
I didn't know what to do
I hid under my duvet

I peeked out
I could see long legs
With only three toes

A long, prickly tail
I could see wings
And big fiery orange eyes

I couldn't see the colour of it
All I could see were great orange eyes
What was it?

Why was it here?

I named it
The Shadow Monster.

Mischa Jayaram (10)
Eveline Day School, Tooting

My Pet Monster

The pet monster is always making pranks
He's scary and furry, he has six hands
When I go to fetch him, he is never home
When I see him, he is always alone
I hate it when he is sad
So I always tickle him under his chin
When I am late, he shrinks down
And hides in a tin
He likes hide-and-seek and he always peeks
I say, "That's cheating!"
But he's always peeking
I always lay him on his bed
When I do that, he looks like he's dead
He follows God's laws
But doesn't like the chores
He is cold-blooded
But never gets old.

Shawn Daniels (7)
Eveline Day School, Tooting

The Last Night

I stepped forward into an open space
I saw a shadow in the distance
I heard something
"This is your last night..."
A weird-looking creature appeared from the
shadows
Its tongue pointing out
Its teeth pitch-black
Its muscles crawling up my back
I stepped back and leaned on a wall
I was sure it was my last night
I was sure I would be lying
Next to my grandma on the graveyard
I closed my eyes
I could only see a monster
And then I knew I would die leaning on a wall
But all I heard was, "Do you want to play?"

Zahra Zafar (11)
Eveline Day School, Tooting

Temper

I know a monster called Temper
I know where he lives
He lives inside all of us
And fiery anger he gives

He is crimson but dark and stormy
And he is boiling to touch
He could flare up at any moment
The hatred released is too much

He can burn and bubble inside you
Like lava spewing out
Until he reaches his highest peak
And you rant, flail and shout

To stop this raging monster exploding
Take deep breaths and count to ten
And calmness closes in and envelopes
He is defeated again.

Stanley Taylor (10)
Eveline Day School, Tooting

A Monster Coming At Night

I'm a very scary monster
When I come and get you at night
I eat everything in sight
I will eat you if you wake up
And I'll know if you wake up or not
So you'd better go to sleep and don't make a peep
If you make a peep, I will eat you
Juicy and spicy is my favourite food

I can always hear you
If I hide in a cave
If you enter my cave
I will like juicy meat
I am really very clever
I will never forget where you live
After I have you for my food
I will hide under the bed.

Aaron Beedassee (8)
Eveline Day School, Tooting

The Witching Hour

Ding-dong!
The clock struck midnight
The witching hour
I hid under my bed
Creak!
My door opened
Before me, there was a hideous sight
Before me stood a bat-like creature with long,
skinny legs
Glowing discs for eyes
Black wings and an evil, sinister smile
"Hello," it said while sniffing the air
"I know you are here somewhere!" it called in a
deep, sing-song voice
My chest was pounding
It spotted me and walked towards me
I knew then I was done for...

Arthur Leake (11)
Eveline Day School, Tooting

The Zapper

I hear crackling noises coming from downstairs
Making me scared and tickling my hairs
I know what he's come for, I know what he's come to see
He's come to steal our supply of electricity

He just rampaged through the door
Like a bull running at a matador
With spiky hair and an electric body
And massive electric antennae guns

He disappears into the night
The house is no longer bright
Sitting in the gloomy dark
We see the Zapper
Create lightning from a single spark.

Ronnie Darroch-Davies (8)
Eveline Day School, Tooting

Slimeball!

He's slimy, disgusting, horrible and weird
But remember, he doesn't have a beard

Slippery and smelly when squeezed
Be careful if he has sneezed

He's a one-eyed, fanged creature with an antenna
He doesn't need an umbrella

He squelches when he slithers across the ground
Squelch! Squelch! Squelch!
Oops! There's a belch!

He smells like unwashed feet
And rolls like a football when kicked through the
street
He's Slimeball!

Rahul Mackinlay (9)
Eveline Day School, Tooting

Secret Monster

Early in the morning
I heard the floorboards creak
I heard a *beep, beep, beep*
I quickly turned on the light
But there was no one in sight
I crouched behind the door
But all I saw was a mouse
I went down the stairs
And all I saw was a trail of hairs
It led me to the kitchen
I took a peep but it was just a shadow
I went upstairs and I started to think
That I was only dreaming
So beware of the secret monster
When your back is turned.

Beatrice Starling (7)
Eveline Day School, Tooting

Flykind

There's a monster in my room
It goes *boom! Boom!*
I creep out onto the landing
To see who is pounding
But then I notice that no one's there
Then, in a gasp of air
Something appears in a flash of light
Then the thing says, "Please take a flight."
So I jump on her back
First, we go straight into the laundry rack
Then off with a whoosh, we went out into the sky
She said, "I love to fly."
So did I.

Beatrice Murphy (7)
Eveline Day School, Tooting

This Is My Monster

I am bubblegum
I am soft
I like to chew gum
I am cuddly
And I am blue

I may be small
But I am brave
I have a big imagination
I am fierce
And I like the colour yellow
I make a squeak
And take a peek
At the lovely city
Very unique and loud
Until I find her in this house
It's quite loud sometimes
But it's very nice
I love my monster
No matter what!

Alix Crawley (8)
Eveline Day School, Tooting

Book Monster

The book monster will eat you
When he eats, he will recognise
The tasty, yummy children tonight
He will eat you today at night
Only if you go in his sight
You'll be stuck in a book
Only if you go in his sight
You'll be published in the Book of Doom
You'll wake in his mouth in the morning
Tonight, he'll chomp you
If you wake up, you'll get to be his yummy food
tonight.

Zain Zafar (7)
Eveline Day School, Tooting

Making Friends With A Monster

It was a dark and misty night
The moon and stars were covered in thick clouds
I could only see its shadow glowing in the dark

It came closer and closer and finally revealed itself
It had three stripy horns
Its fur felt like sheep's wool

Everyone was hiding away from it
Except me
We made friends and I never forgot him.

Maria Kostyleva (8)
Eveline Day School, Tooting

Predator

There's a monster lurking on the street
I don't know what he's doing
But he always comes back to me
He lives in a flying saucer
Way up above my street
He may look horrifying
But he is very nice and sweet
When he comes to visit
He seems very hungry so
I give him lots of meat
After, he's very happy.

Leo Thomas Brannan (8)
Eveline Day School, Tooting

Wretched Ground

The corruptadon is as light as the sun
My monster is as dangerous as a stampede.
It burrows underground and follows your steps
Then suddenly, the ground under your feet falls
and you get eaten by the corruptadon.
The corruptadon is as happy as anything
And the corruptadon lays its eggs and rolls to its
mate at its deadly home
And when the baby corruptadon hatches, the cycle
starts again
And now you might be its next victim
But nobody can know without an X-ray.
Nobody survives it until there is mega technology.
But it's not that simple.
Corruptadons evolve as well
So get prepared for the war.
There might be severe damage to humans, so have
good luck
For the extinction of humans or corruptadons.

Hugo Dziemiach (8)
Giles Junior School, Stevenage

The Adventures Of Baby Boo Boo

B aby Boo Boo is as cute as a newborn baby
A s sparkly as a troll and disco ball
B ody as yellow as a sunshine
Y ells when scared

B lue as the sky stripes
"O ooooo," said Baby Boo Boo
"O ooooo," said Baby Boo Boo

B aby Boo Boo loves soft, squishy cuddles
"O h, I love soft cuddles!"
O h, you'll love Baby Boo Boo

He's as fluffy as a giant teddy bear
He is as happy as a troll
He lives in a doll's house
When he comes out, he goes to normal size.

Amelia Eggleton (9)
Giles Junior School, Stevenage

Kaykay The Monster

K illed elephants

A vicious monster

Y ellow, red, blue

K aykay is a killing machine

A war monster

Y ou have been warned

T errifying

H unting lava

E nd the reign of Kaykay

M unching

O n the edge of mountains

N ormally, they break down

S torms are no match for him

T en weapons aren't enough

E ven a thousand isn't enough

R un!

Kayden Nel (7)

Giles Junior School, Stevenage

Farticus Mcdonald

Tiptoeing through a haunted house,
I heard a *woooooooo, wooo*, then a scream and
then a cackle,
Then I closed my eyes and looked behind me
slowly,
My eyes lit up because I saw a bright light,
Am I seeing things? Am I crazy? Is this a dream?

Out came a huge wing, I was scared,
It smelled of fart and toilet paper mixed together,
He looked green and had two massive spikes on
the top of his head,
It did a massive pop, *blarp!*
Revealing his stinky self,

And then,
Blarp!

Max James Matthew Borer (8)
Giles Junior School, Stevenage

Eric

My monster likes being called Eric,
Eric looks like my dojo monster,
Eric likes to eat slime,
Eric smells like pork sausages,
Eric moves like a baby sloth,
Eric is as grey as a koala bear.
Eric's teeth are as white as a cloud,
Eric dances like a giraffe,
Eric waves like a person to his friends,
Eric has black spots like my dojo monster,
Eric has big, bulgy eyes as big as a funny
caterpillar,
Eric's ears are as great as a koala bear,
Eric smiles as big as a happy person.

Samuel Holton-Fox (7)

Giles Junior School, Stevenage

Monster From The Cave

Monster from the cave,
Running through a cave.
I saw skulls and brains.
Just then, I heard a hiss.
I quickly faced the entrance of a never-ending
cave.
I thought something,
Is there something here or am I hearing things?

Just then, a scaly red tail popped out.
It smelt like blue cheese.
It was covered in sticks and stones.
Just then, his legs, arms and his eyes looked
mysteriously.
I ran and it jumped on me.
He showed his green, bloody teeth.

Tommy de-Vall (8)
Giles Junior School, Stevenage

Haunted HQ Look Out

E lectric poison
L etting poison out
E ating poison
C utting wires in half
T raining like a ninja
R oaring as loud as an aeroplane
I n a deadly HQ, he
C an shoot out

P oisonous blades
O n the top of the blades are zappers
I n the suit is a
S pike trap
O n its suit is a minigun
N oisily shooting 10,000 bullets.

Viktor Krasniqi (7)
Giles Junior School, Stevenage

Monsters Everywhere

M y friend walks around at night.

O nly on Christmas and Halloween nights.

N ot on Easter or any other holidays.

S o come down and see him, he won't bite.

T o whoever reads this poem, my monster is called Mitch.

E ggs he likes to eat, especially chocolate.

R ed, red eyes he has. This might make him look scary, but he's not.

S ome say he's nice, some say he's mean.

Megan Green (8)
Giles Junior School, Stevenage

Monster From A Pitch-Black Candy Factory

Wandering through a pitch-black candy factory,
I heard something behind me,
Slowly, I turned to face pitch-black.
Am I hearing something or is it just me?
Is there someone there?
Just then, out stepped a big furry leg,
Covered in candy and melted chocolate,
As some of it appeared and disappeared.
Its eyes looked like as red as a rose.
It pounced at me fast, revealing razor-sharp teeth.

Madison Parker (8)
Giles Junior School, Stevenage

The Haunted Junkyard Monster

Sneaking into a haunted junkyard
I heard a *whoosh, zoom, bang* behind me
Slowly, I turned around, but there was nothing
Am I dreaming? Am I something's prey?
After, I saw a huge, rusty wheel.
One red eye popped out
And a sharp grey claw
With two red sharp creepy horns!

I saw its shadow getting bigger and bigger
Then it charged at me
Revealing its razor-sharp, red-as-blood teeth
And its missiles...

Zachary Agbenya (9)
Giles Junior School, Stevenage

The Galaxy Monster

Whoosh! I heard a shocking noise.
I was shaking from beneath my feet.
I stepped down my bed's ladder.
I looked under my bed.
I found... a monster!
Its body was pinkish-purple, its eyes were sparkly emerald-green.

It wrapped itself around me!
It was very gentle.
Her cheeks were glowing red.
She had a galaxy horn.
She was super magical.
She was very kind and easy to find.

My monster's name was Victoria.

Mackayla Korsah (8)
Giles Junior School, Stevenage

The Dobby Monster

Wandering through the secret place I found,
I heard a sound behind me.
Slowly, I turned around to only see empty
darkness.
Am I in a dream, is this real?
Just then, stepping out from behind the tree,
A very slimy leg covered in sticky mud and dry
leaves
As it came out slowly from behind the tree,
Its eyes looked like fire, it pounced at me
Revealing its sharp teeth.

Maja Slaczalek (8)

Giles Junior School, Stevenage

The City Monster

Walking through the dark candy land world,
I heard a clank, whoosh and a rustle behind,
Slowly, I turned to see nothing but darkness.
Is this real? Am I dreaming?
Just then stepped out a long, furry leg
Covered in noodles and newspapers.
As it flew out of the shadows,
Its eyes were pink and cute.
It happily jumped onto me and smiled,
Revealing its flat, sparkly teeth at me.

Ethan Hudson (8)
Giles Junior School, Stevenage

The McGreedy

Walking into McDonald's, I heard a noise.
I slowly walked over to an empty table.
Shall I sit down on this table? What shall I do?
Just then, the creature said, "Grrrr!"
He smelled horrible and he had seven big googly eyes.
The creature came towards me with tomato sauce on his teeth.
It jumped onto me and made me fall over,
Revealing his skunk tail.

Millie Bartlett (8)
Giles Junior School, Stevenage

Bubble-Bop

B ubbles go everywhere in the house,
U p the stairs, everywhere in the bed,
B *ang!* What was that downstairs?
B alloons go pop in the garden,
L aughing out loud,
E lephant toy, I say what.

B ig cuddles, I love it,
O ff he goes in the lovely blue sky,
P op bubbles in the air.

Noah Jennings (8)
Giles Junior School, Stevenage

I Wandered Through The Woods

I wandered through the woods.

Wandering through the deep woods,
I heard a rustling behind me,
Slowly, I turned to face only empty darkness.
Am I hearing things? Is there something out there?

Just then stepped out a vast, furry leg covered in dirty mud.
As it drifted out of the shadows,
Its eyes looked fierce.
Suddenly, it pounced,
Revealing its very sharp teeth...

Charmaine Coleman (8)
Giles Junior School, Stevenage

The Coloured Balls

One day a colour ball came to paint.
It looked fluffy and it was friendly.
It held its colour ball which changed the colour of
his fur.
They are funny when they jump.
They lose their ball.
They can run fast.
They live in pots.
They live for 100 years.
They are pets.
They are little helpers.
They can come in blue, rainbow, green, red, yellow,
pink.
The rarest is grey.

Christian Ventour (8)

Giles Junior School, Stevenage

The Jibberish Monster

This monster you may see, she is silent all day long
But she talks jibberish all night long
She is as fluffy as a ball of cotton and she takes
me on a ride on her back
And did I forget to tell you she has wings?
In return, I give her lots of sausages and meat to
eat.
She has the biggest wings and the softest wings.
She is as big as a fan.
She is coloured yellow.

Josie Magdinier (8)
Giles Junior School, Stevenage

The Bang Battler

I was walking through a pitch-black forest,
I heard a bang from behind me.
I turned around as slow as a slug to see pitch-blackness.
Is there something there?

Then a dark red eye appeared from nowhere,
The eye was like lava with a black island in it.
As it crept out from behind a rock,
It pounced forward like a tiger,
Revealing its razor-sharp body.

Jacob Waters (9)
Giles Junior School, Stevenage

Super Red Jelly

M y monster is called Super Red Jelly.

O n hot days, he comes out.

N ow, don't tell anyone.

S tay away from red caves or he will burn you

T wo people have been near a red cave.

E very time someone goes near it, they get burnt

R obots have been sent to get him, but they run off.

Reuben Fraser (8)

Giles Junior School, Stevenage

The Shape-Shifter Monster!

I was jogging on the mountain tops,
I heard footsteps behind me,
I quickly turned around but only saw my shadow,
Am I imagining things? Is anything there?
Immediately, a big scaly tail popped out,
It smelt like mint,
It then waddled out of the darkness,
It had blunt claws but sharp teeth,
Just then, it crawled on me,
Revealing its evil smile.

Ryxa Sofia Golez (8)
Giles Junior School, Stevenage

The Wood Monster

Wandering through the forest,
Suddenly, I saw a vast brown leg step out
Amongst the overgrown weeds.
Just then, I saw this beast destroy a house!
Then I realised that this beast from hell
Was, in fact, coming straight towards me at speed,
I felt terrified!
But then I heard a bolt of lighting.
Am I dreaming? I thought to myself.

Joseph Thompson (9)
Giles Junior School, Stevenage

The Kidnapper

Skipping through the woods,
I heard a squeak behind,
Slowly I turned, but all I saw
Was the empty darkness.
Am I hearing things or is it just me?

Just then, I saw a piece of strange hair.
It was pink, but a very weird sort of pink.
Then a white and fluffy leg came out.
Its eyes were red and bloody as a rose.

Zofia Paszkiet (8)
Giles Junior School, Stevenage

Monster Behind Me

Walking through the woods,
I heard the bushes behind starting to shake.

Slowly, I turned around to see what it was.
Am I hearing this? Is something there?

Just then, a vast, scaly leg.
It smelt of something revolting.
Its eyes were fierce and dark red.
It pounced and bounced at me,
Revealing its ziggy, zaggy teeth.

Brooke Booth (9)
Giles Junior School, Stevenage

The Monster In The Woods

I was wandering through the dark woods.
I heard something rustling.
I slowly turned around to the dark.
Am I hearing things? Is there anyone out there?
Just then stepped out a scaly leg,
Covered in mud and leaves.
As it looked out of the shadows,
Its eyes looked dark red.
It jumped at me with razor-sharp teeth...

Alfie Harris (8)

Giles Junior School, Stevenage

The 3am Monster

Walking through the giant dump,
I heard a big bang behind me,
Very slowly, I turned to face a pile of scrap metal.
Am I in a dream? What was that?

Just then stepped out a thick, scaly leg,
That smelt like a skunk's butt.
As it walked out, its belly looked like a ball of fur.
It jumped at me, revealing his fat face.

Vinny Gary Murray (8)
Giles Junior School, Stevenage

Slimy Ball

Skipping happily into the dark cave,
I heard a sudden bang ahead of me!
Quickly, I ran towards a light.
Is this real or am I dreaming?

Suddenly, I saw two glowing blue eyes,
Glowing like the sunset.
As it jumped out from behind a crystal,
Its legs looked weird and slimy.
It leapt for me,
Revealing its tiny four legs.

Evie Bladd (8)
Giles Junior School, Stevenage

Scaly Monster

Wandering through the park, I heard a thump!
I slowly walked into a wood.
Is this real or am I dreaming?

Suddenly, I saw a big, scaly, sharp arm
Sticking out behind a tree!
It slowly started to come out from behind the tree.
It was slimy and slippery,
But just then, it came out the tree
And pounced at me!

Christiana Stainton (9)
Giles Junior School, Stevenage

Bowser The Big Monster

Bowser likes to play dodgeball, but his friends call
it modgeball
They all teamed up to destroy the world
They threw a meteor to make it twirl
He calls people meanies and drools on their heads
He likes to steal blankets off of people's beds
He likes to wrestle his friends
One of his friends is called Ben.

Jamie-Lee Hlasi
Giles Junior School, Stevenage

The Cave Monster

Wandering through the long cave,
I heard a roar behind,
Quickly, I turned to only see a grey wall,
Is this really true? Am I dreaming things?

Just then, a tiny wing popped out,
Covered in wet,
As it slowly went out of the shadows,
Its eyes looked scary,
It pounced at me,
Revealing its sharp teeth.

Isabelle Headland (8)
Giles Junior School, Stevenage

The Mystery Monster

I was peering through the fluffy clouds and
I spotted an unknown house.
I glanced into it,
I tried to find a light switch.
It was pitch-dark and it was creepy.
I saw ruby red eyes come out of the shadows.

It tried to pounce.
I quickly moved.
It had razor-sharp teeth,
Ruby-red eyes,
Razor-sharp claws.

Riley Cook (8)
Giles Junior School, Stevenage

Monster

Hilarious
Elephant-looking
Donkey head
Lives in an igloo
Eats donkey to get donkey's head
Has a monster head
Has monster feet on its head

M oisture liquid.
O range gobblers.
N ever slimy.
S leepy and smelly.
T errifying breath.
E xhausting gums.
R azor claws.

Avijit Tirumalasetti (7)
Giles Junior School, Stevenage

Monster From The Temple

Walking through the temple,
I heard a loud clashing noise,
I slowly turned around to where the noise came from,
What was that?

Just then, I saw two scaly legs pop out,
It smelt like blood,
As it drifted out the darkness,
Its eye was fierce and red,
It jumped at me,
Revealing its four razor-sharp teeth.

Oliver Crisp (8)
Giles Junior School, Stevenage

The Changewing

C hasing fish
H igh in the sky
A s he dives
N ever staying dry
G etting very wet
E ven in the lake
W hen he jumps out, he makes a big splash
I wish I could ride him
N ight and day
G o, dragon, go!

William Jackson (7)
Giles Junior School, Stevenage

My Monster

My monster is as big as a double-decker bus
My monster is as hairy as a gorilla
My monster likes to eat some fish and chips
My monster can fly as high as a jet plane
My monster likes to play at the park
My monster likes to play on the Xbox
My monster likes to eat food and likes to eat
breakfast.

Joshua Howes (7)
Giles Junior School, Stevenage

Into The Forest

Wandering through a giant forest,
I heard a ghostly sound.
Slowly, I turned to darkness.
Am I actually hearing this? Am I hearing things?
A tail poked out, a white tail.
Just then, white arms came out from the trees.
It slowly flew over to me,
Revealing its razor-sharp teeth.

Noah Whitehouse (8)
Giles Junior School, Stevenage

Monster In Sand

Walking on the beach,
I saw a sand lump come out of nowhere.
I slowly approached with caution.
Am I seeing things? What is going on?
Just then, a head popped out, covered in seaweed
And two more heads popped up,
Covered in red seaweed with razor-sharp teeth.

Oliver O'Keeffe (8)
Giles Junior School, Stevenage

Green Boy

G reater like a bull
R ed like a fire
E veryone hates him
E vening runner
N aughty guy

B ad person
O melette-hater
Y o-yo-eater

A fast-runner
A human-eater
A great-footballer
A cup-winner
A great-goalie
A karate-dreamer.

Archie Edwards (8)
Giles Junior School, Stevenage

Creepy Monster

I wandered through the deep, dark woods,
Suddenly, I heard a creepy sound.
I was scared!
Then when I said hello,
A monster leapt out from the deep, dark cave,
Then the monster jumped on top of me,
Then it licked me, so then I said, "I will take you home."

Joel Osadi (8)
Giles Junior School, Stevenage

Angry Ethan

M onsters
O n my house
N asty
S illy
T errifying
E *ek!*
R un!

E xcellent
T oo smart
H eroic
A wfully happy
N ipping people.

Nathaniel Korsah (7)
Giles Junior School, Stevenage

Bug's Army

In the desert, Bug threw his dreadful spear
Which was as sharp as a wolf's claw
Then suddenly, his enemy Destroyer appeared
"One shall fall!" said Bug
"You're right," grumbled Destroyer
"I have an army," laughed Bug.

Tom Davison (7)
Giles Junior School, Stevenage

Redclaw

The claws of Redclaw
Redclaw is very fast.
When you are running, he will run past you.
Be very careful with Redclaw.
He has sharp fangs in his jaws.
Redclaw smells like lollipops
But do not make him mad
As he hisses when he thinks you are bad.

Charlie Scott (7)

Giles Junior School, Stevenage

Monster

M onday munching on snacks

O n a Tuesday morning, there is someone behind you

N o one in my room

S even eyes looking at you

T ime to run

E *ek!*

R *oar!*

Kea'Rae Caroline Quinlan (7)
Giles Junior School, Stevenage

The Night Star

My monster's name is called Rainbow
I saw, with my own eyes, something quick go past
me.
He was really soft when I touched him.
When I looked at him, he was really adorable.
He was good at fighting and it was like riding a
scary lion.

Emily Thomas (8)
Giles Junior School, Stevenage

My Pet Werewolves

In the woods, there was a pack of wolves.
Suddenly, it became night-time
And the wolves turned into werewolves!
The werewolves had teeth as sharp as a chainsaw
and claws as big as a tree.
They could run as fast as 300,055 miles per hour.

Harry Verschuren (7)
Giles Junior School, Stevenage

My Monster

I have a little monster living down my street.
I take it lots of ice cream and sweets to eat.
Sometimes, I invite her in to play
And she stays for the whole day!
She gives me a ride on her giant wings
In return, she asks me to sing!

Lola Grace Rosenwink (8)
Giles Junior School, Stevenage

The Chocolate Flying Snakes

The chocolate flying snakes.
Walking through the deep wood slowly,
I heard loud hisses coming from behind me,
I slowly turned around to see the empty darkness.
I said to myself, "Am I hearing things?
Or is there a ghost?"

Niamh Cahill-Testouri (8)
Giles Junior School, Stevenage

DJ

There's a monster living down my street
He only comes out at night
He's a bone-muncher and a tongue-licker
He has a fang as sharp as a razor
Sharp claws and it likes to be named DJ
He's as tall as a double-decker bus.

Mikey Sapsford (7)
Giles Junior School, Stevenage

Monster

M assive claws
O range eyes and breath
N aughty and lost in the forest
S tinky cheese claws
T oys to play with
E asy knobbly walk
R oar like a dinosaur.

Jared Aitken (7)
Giles Junior School, Stevenage

Monsters Everywhere

Pow! I heard a noise, I tiptoed downstairs
As I got closer and closer, it got louder

I was finally downstairs
Then I heard the kitchen door slam

I slowly opened the door
It was a slimy monster, his name was Joey.

Alfie James Newman (8)
Giles Junior School, Stevenage

Monster

M ysterious follower

O tter eye

N ot a nosey monster

S melly scary monster

T wo-nosed monster

E ggy-smelling fire

R ed radioactive fire.

Maya Wegner (7)
Giles Junior School, Stevenage

The Wind

A whoosh on my window
What is that doing?
Who is here?
I don't know what was there
But I found a monster

I will show you
It has wings like birds
A head of a dog
A body like a cat
I let it go back out.

Jeremy Garcia (8)
Giles Junior School, Stevenage

My Monster

My monster is as scary as a wolf.
My monster is as tall as a tower.
My monster slithers along like a snake.
His claws are as sharp as a knife.
He can run as fast as a raptor when he's chasing his prey.

Ozzy Chace Dyer (7)
Giles Junior School, Stevenage

The Night Dark Hearing

S *hush!*
H is ears are small
A ll is okay
D on't cry
"O w! Why did you hit me, monster?"
"W hat? I did not!"

Nana Adom Akyampong (7)
Giles Junior School, Stevenage

Nancy The Devil

Roar! I hear a noise like a lion.
I go down the stairs
To see a hideous creature.
She has sharp, spiky spikes.
She has orange and red skin.
Her name is Nancy the devil.
She is my best friend.

Amelie Morgan (8)
Giles Junior School, Stevenage

Vicious Monster

B ubbly monsters
U nfair
B ook-lover
B ubblegum-lover
L ibrary-
E ater
G olden
U nhappy
M ean monster.

Lacey Lou Wales (8)
Giles Junior School, Stevenage

Beware, Bane Is There

My monster is called Bane.
He feels no pain.
He crushes his fingers together
And lives wherever.
If you show no fear
He will land right here.
If it's clear, you can start walking and talking.

Harrison Brown (8)
Giles Junior School, Stevenage

Naughty Monsters Poem

M ucky monsters eating pizza
O n a Monday at school
N aughty monster
S noring loudly
T ime to wake up
E *ek!*
R un!

Gracie-Mae Faulkner (7)

Giles Junior School, Stevenage

Clesna

C laws razor-sharp.

L ong and hairy tail

E ndangered creature.

S avage sometimes.

N ever go near it.

A ngry and dangerous sometimes.

Bobby Johnson (7)
Giles Junior School, Stevenage

Evil

My monster runs as fast as a cheetah.
My monster is as big as a school.
My monster can fly as high as an aeroplane.
My monster has a name...
Its name is Evil,
But it's as cute as a kitten.

Phoebe Parker (7)
Giles Junior School, Stevenage

My Giant Monster Is Called Cake

My giant monster is called Cake
He is as round as a lemon
He is as cute as a cat
He looks like a pet
He is like a big ball of fluff
He is a good boy and he likes playing
He likes football.

Bailey Ryan Carter (8)
Giles Junior School, Stevenage

Monster

M onsters are scary

O gres are friends with monsters

N ot scared of anything

S cratchy thing

T rouble for others

E lephant-eater

R abbit-nibbler.

Felicite Joy (7)

Giles Junior School, Stevenage

Monster

M assive scary monster.

O ver its prey.

N asty teeth.

S cary, slithering monster.

T iny teaser.

E ating deadly.

R ound, chubby belly.

Bobby Moffat (8)

Giles Junior School, Stevenage

Monster

M arvellous sharp claws.

O range fire eyes.

N ever doing good things.

S cary creature.

T remendous feet.

E normous ears.

R aggy tail.

David Neagu (7)

Giles Junior School, Stevenage

Excellent Ethan

E xcellent Ethan

T ired and needs some rest

H e has razor blade claws

A nd it's waking up time

N ow it's time to run!

Waleed Ahmad (7)

Giles Junior School, Stevenage

Monster

M ystery mind

O range eyes

N ose of black

S melly breath

T errifying wail

E ggy teeth

R ed curly hair.

Eliza Jane Harrison (7)

Giles Junior School, Stevenage

My Name Is Theo

My monster is as small as an ant.
My monsters teeth are as sharp as a pin.
My monster moves like the Flash.
My monster dives into the trash
And my monster loves rotten fish.

Theo Barbet (7)
Giles Junior School, Stevenage

Beware There Is A Monster Over There

My monster is as soft as silk.
Soft as a pom-pom.
He is short and cuddly like a baby bear.
He is as kind as a puppy!
He lives in a kitchen cupboard.
His name is... Spot!

Taylin Large (8)
Giles Junior School, Stevenage

Bob The Monster

Bob is as deadly as a zombie.
Bob's teeth are as sharp as a shark's tooth.
He is as fast as a raptor.
He eats dogs all day long.
His tummy is as big as a house.

Mikah Demetrio Jay Richards (8)
Giles Junior School, Stevenage

My Monster

His ears as red as a shiny apple.
My monster is as fast as a wolf.
My monster is as scary as a tiger.
He is as tall as a tower.
My monster is fluffy like a cat.

Poppie Grant-Richardson (7)
Giles Junior School, Stevenage

Monster

M assive

O range hair

N est-eater

S cary teeth

T errible toes

E gg-chomper

R ock-biter.

Lucas Wojtas (7)

Giles Junior School, Stevenage

My Monster Poem

My monster is fluffy.
My monster is a bunny.
My bunny is eating cookies.
My monster is funny, silly, hungry and spotty.

Aimee W (8)
Giles Junior School, Stevenage

Monster

M unching

O range eyes

N aughty

S oft fur

T errifying claws

E ating all day

R eally tired.

Honey Star Richmond-Turner (7)

Giles Junior School, Stevenage

Lucy The Star

I see a monster living in my street,
I bring it cereal for it to eat.
I love to see him every day,
I love the way he flies away.

Shayla Lucy Timms (7)
Giles Junior School, Stevenage

Safire

S quelchy
A te people
F eet are stinky
I t is disgusting
R aging roar
E ggy feet.

Jack Maxwell-Reeve (7)

Giles Junior School, Stevenage

Monster

A kennings poem

A mouse-chaser.
A milk-drinker.
A paw-licker.
A quiet-meower.
An ear-twitcher.
A fast runner.

Amelie Rose Liversidge (7)
Giles Junior School, Stevenage

My Monster

A kennings poem

A water-drinker.
A milk-drinker.
A doughnut-eater.
A slow-walker.
A good-climber.
Appearing.

Ella Clayson (8)

Giles Junior School, Stevenage

Bella The Monster

A kennings poem

Bella the monster
A cute ballerina
A mud chomper
A great helper
A fantastic flier.

Anya Arbon
Giles Junior School, Stevenage

The Monster Called Baggy

M y monster's name is Baggy but it's also nasty

O ver his head, there's heavy horns and prawns on top

N o one has ever hurt him because he's really stealthy

S top him, you won't because he has really heavy tops

T he monster is really not scary, but it is really hairy

E veryone thinks the monster is furry

R eally, the monster is silly and its name is called Nilly.

Joseph Jackson (8)
Haxby Road Primary School, York

Rofi

In the night, she will open her mouth
To gobble her lunch
And then she will have fun
Her hair is a tiny speck
Her horns are like flames
And her body is as soft as a sheep
Her eyes are like the natural blue sky
That is lovely and bright
Her mouth is wide open
To gobble her lunch
If you see a green furball
It is a monster.

Sahasra Thotakura (7)
Haxby Road Primary School, York

My Cute Little Monster

My cute monster's name is Twinkles
She brings home drops of sparkly sprinkles
Her favourite food has to be stardust
Anything else she looks at in disgust
Little Twinkles is really cute
But she uses her mouth in the opposite of mute
My cutie monster's name is Twinkles
Her very best friend's name is Sparkly Sprinkles.

Lois Rycroft (8)
Haxby Road Primary School, York

Greeny

He likes to have his food made out of wood
His toes look like a nose
His eyes scare flies
His teeth meet sheep
His mouth glows with a rainbow
His nose will take a doze
He has nails in the mail
He lives in the zoo and that's true
He glows blue and has a tattoo.

Leo Wood (8)
Haxby Road Primary School, York

My Monster

The ears are colourful like a rainbow
The red nose shines like a rose
The bulging eyes glow bright
The rotten teeth glow at night.

Teagan Mia Smith (8)
Haxby Road Primary School, York

Lonely Leah

The wind was howling in the breeze
In the distance, you could see
Something like a wild yeti
Nobody knew what it was
Some people said it was a wild animal
Others said a very hairy person
But it was really a monster
The monster was fluffy, hungry and lonely
It was roaming around the forest
Looking for something to eat
This type of monster only eats meat
Snap! went some twigs
This monster went to a farm to munch on some pigs
All the animals were asleep
I should not repeat
Now he must have some food
He must leave.

Victoria McGinn (11)
Onthank Primary School, Kilmarnock

Furious Folter

Furious Folter is a huge fiery beast
For his dinner, he always has a big feast
He is as giant as a massive evil castle
He is very selfish and causes everyone hassle
Boom! as he crashes through the town
Roar! as the fire blasts from his mouth
Fiery like lava
Everything, everyone, even the buildings are
shaking in fear
Some people even let out a little tear
He swings down with his huge, giant wings
As the people say, "Oh jings!"
Furious Folter isn't that nice
Just watch out, it's a bit of advice.

Joe Henry Dudgeon (11)
Onthank Primary School, Kilmarnock

Death Striker

When it's ten o'clock at night
It's the time that children get a fright
He's spotty and blue
And he likes to watch you
He is as hungry as a tiger
And I can't bet you a fiver
Watch out!

He could be hiding outside
So you'd better hide
He likes to eat children as delicious food
He is always in the perfect mood
He can't fit under the bed
He's big, like I said
So, as he starts to open the door
He can hear the children snore
He will walk over to your bed
And rip off your head!

Matthew O'Hare (11)
Onthank Primary School, Kilmarnock

Scary Scarlett

I could hear a growl under my bed
I could see the slime oozing out of my bed that
was red
I felt big, sharp horns graze against my hand
Stomp! Stomp!
Suddenly, she was standing right there
Her teeth were as sharp as freshly sharpened
knives
Slime was still oozing out of her hands
She grabbed my teddy
Chomp! Chomp!
As she ate it all up
Her arms were as thin as my pencil
Her horns looked like utensils
She was as purple as a juicy plum
Her teeth were as red as a ripe cherry.

Neve Robertson (11)
Onthank Primary School, Kilmarnock

Little Sid

At ten o'clock at night
You need to look right
To make sure he does not bite
He is big, hungry and naughty, he will give you a
fright
He is that hungry, he could eat 100 chicken
nuggets
So he looks for kids that have buckets
He will come and get you if you make a noise
And he will step over your toys

Sid will come and get you and gobble you up
His stomach will erupt
If he doesn't eat kids by ten o'clock at night
You could be getting a visit
You might get a fright!

Ellie Kerr (11)
Onthank Primary School, Kilmarnock

Colourful Cathy

In the night, you'd better be careful
Because an evil monster is lurking
She might be colourful, she might look nice
But Cathy will give you a huge fright
Stay in your house, stay in your room
Unless you want to die tonight
Look out, she's in your house
She can be as quiet as a mouse
So you should lock your doors and stay under the covers
As a horrifying monster is coming
So you should be careful, you should watch out
As Colourful Cathy is coming, so stay in your house!

Olivia Cooper (11)
Onthank Primary School, Kilmarnock

Spiky Sean

One day, the wind was soaring, it was so boring
Spiky Sean slowly and steadily slithered down the street
His spikes were as sharp as kites
He may look quite friendly, but if you make him mad
He could get quite needy
Spiky Sean's beaming red eyes are getting closer
Watch out

Keep your eyes closed without a doubt
Spooky Scary Sean
Spooky Scary Sean
You should always sleep with one eye open
Otherwise, you might regret it
When the clock hits 12pm, Sean will strike!

Rhys Krupp (11)
Onthank Primary School, Kilmarnock

Bog

Bog was standing in the shade
His teeth were as sharp as a well-crafted blade
He had two giant, gleaming, scary eyes
He had a great big mouth, so he was good at
telling lies
He was as slimy as a big fat slug
He accidentally stood on Sam's grumpy pug
Creak! As Bog snuck through the house
Bog was as quiet as a small, quiet mouse
Tiptoe, tiptoe, tiptoe up to Sam's bed
Roar! Yum! Yum! Yum! Now Sam was dead!

Miller Davidson (11)
Onthank Primary School, Kilmarnock

Where Did Blobby Go?

Once upon a time, Blobby the shorty
He was friends with a Krabby Patty
Then he was a big mouth
Because he ate a moth's mouth
He was furious because of Jeff
Who was eating his jawdropping cubes
He started shrinking
Like a shrimp shining
And he would grow to the size of a house
He wore shorts and then fell
Like a dead cow
And it fell through the floor
And no one saw the blue guy ever again.

Tyler Qua (11)
Onthank Primary School, Kilmarnock

The Shadow Stalker

The Shadow Stalker pouncing through the shade
Waiting for its prey
Its teeth are as sharp as a blade
If you step in the shade, you'll be slain
Before you're killed, they once said
It would tell you, "It was paid
By the person that wants you dead."
Once it's been seen, it fades away

Bang! It smashes your house wall
"Argh!" You wake up and see something tall!

Luke Fairbairn (10)
Onthank Primary School, Kilmarnock

Ned Comes Out For A Bite

On Halloween night
Ned comes out to bite
He thinks for a moment
And then he strikes
Nobody is safe at
This time of night
For his teeth will give you a big fright
His horns are as sharp as a kitchen knife
He is a green, ugly monster
For he is as hideous as a vulture
Well, that's all I can say
For he's coming out to play
Keep your doors locked tight
Or you could die tonight.

Phoebe Black (11)
Onthank Primary School, Kilmarnock

Twilight's Attack

One horrible night
Whoville got a fright

Once the Grinch lost the battle
Twilight came to fight

She was as slimy as a slug
As deadly as ten sharks

Nobody knew she was about
So she could catch her prey easily
Without a doubt

One by one, the children cried
When they got stolen in the dead of night

So watch out, she might come
And give you a fright.

Erin Mary Williams (10)
Onthank Primary School, Kilmarnock

The Death Zenders

Halloween night
The time these creatures fight
When you lie in bed
The Death Zenders could rip off your head
Or break into your homes
And break your bones
They are very small
With a fast crawl
They are hangry
Which is hungry and angry
They will give you a chill
Then get ready to kill
These demented imps
Hate shrimp
So always have some shrimp
To keep back the imps.

Christopher Brown (11)
Onthank Primary School, Kilmarnock

The Bogey Man

The Bogey Man is terrifying
He is an absolute giant
His horns are multicoloured
And his teeth are as well
I know where he got the massive cut
From the mighty whale across the ocean
He eats children for his supper
And for his dessert, he eats a grumpy pupper
But tonight, he is having a moaning mum
He'll rip her head off till
Bill round the corner has a tantrum.

Alex Chudleigh (11)
Onthank Primary School, Kilmarnock

Big Head Bob

I see a cute monster at the side of my bed
I pet it and its eyes go bright red

His arms and legs are like sticks
They're thinner than toothpicks

He's vicious and mad
He makes the children sad

As he creeps through the house
Quiet like a mouse

He's vicious, as I said
Now he's ripping off your head.

Jack Edgar (10)
Onthank Primary School, Kilmarnock

138

The Clown

This horrific creature
Roams for adventure
And eats kids every night
And likes to have a fight
I would not go near this creature
Because he will give you a fright
He has bright red eyes like a devil
So you'd better hope that you are a rebel
He will eat you up
Unless you're ready for a fight
And he will use balloons!

Kyle Hamilton (11)
Onthank Primary School, Kilmarnock

Deadly David

Deadly David is like a thief
With his sharp yellow teeth
And his skull eyes
He will only come out when it's a dark blue sky
He will watch you in your sleep
And he will leave you with a cut that is so deep
He might go for the throat
He is as fast as a goat
Watch out! You might be next!

Kirsten Roberson (11)
Onthank Primary School, Kilmarnock

Mr Big Mouth

Mr Big Mouth, that was his name
Always willing to play a game
He'll gouge your eyes out
Without a doubt
You'd best hide
Because when the tide comes in
He will be out
Don't get up
Don't make a peep
Because Mr Big Mouth is out
To eat...

Carly Inglis (11)
Onthank Primary School, Kilmarnock

Mr Chomp

At the dawn of the day
Mr Chomp comes out to play
Make sure you stay in your bed
His eyes are blood-red
He loves to eat kids
He is not kind
He's not afraid to fight
He will take a bite tonight
Will it be your night?

Morgan Clark (10)
Onthank Primary School, Kilmarnock

All About Crazy Max

Crazy Max is a monster and is a lovely monster
His hair is slimy as snot
His teeth is as sharp as a silver, pointy needle
His necklace is long as a cat's ginger tail
Crazy Max is crazy because he doesn't understand
Spanish
He is friendly because he is a nice monster and he
loves people
His claws are massive, pointy like a shark's teeth
His eyes are brown because he doesn't like any
colour
Only this one

His clothes are blue like diamonds in a dark cave
His horn is so short but he likes it because it's
wonderful
Crazy Max loves to play with amazing children in
the park
Crazy Max is a super monster because he is a nice
monster like others
His head is round like a circle
Crazy Max is a monster who is good.

Emmanuel Dumbuya (7)
Regis Manor Primary School, Milton Regis

My Best Friend, Flufballs

Flufballs has got lots of eyes like an alien
You have never met a monster like Flufballs
Flufballs has four arms with a spotty body and four legs
Flufballs is always hungry because he wants to eat scrumptious children
Who have a lot of blood in them so he can drink it up
You have never seen a monster like Flufballs
Flufballs' favourite food is seaweed sandwich
With sausages and seaweed and mud with carrots and beans
His favourite drink is banana and strawberry mousse
And orange soup with carrots that are muddy
You have never seen a monster like that
Don't get scared - if you do, he is very kind and nice
Don't go near him because he will eat you like a dinosaur chomp
He is as big as a dinosaur because he eats a lot.

Jessica Jane Carter (7)
Regis Manor Primary School, Milton Regis

All About Spike

Spike is gigantic and has horns as sharp as a
hedgehog's spike
He has sharp jaws so he can eat delicious,
scrumptious children
He is scary, naughty, nice and lethal
He roams through the eerie night, waiting for
children's snores
Make sure he doesn't see you or you will end up
between his jaws
Spike thinks children are treats because the blood
tastes good to him
So watch out, stay under your covers
Because Spike is looking for children to be asleep
He is as hungry as a male lion
His favourite food is children
Spike has a lethal touch at the end of his tail
His claws are so sharp that he can break a strong
brick wall
Spike's breath smells like rotten eggs.

Grace Charley-Beth Evans (7)
Regis Manor Primary School, Milton Regis

All About Snakey!

Snakey is as green as jelly
Snakey is also really stinky like sewage
Snakey's breath smells like a rotten apple
His jaws are as strong and smelly as bones
Also, his arms are squishy like jelly
His socks are as stinky as mouldy cheese
My monster is taller than the Eiffel Tower
Snakey's tongue is as black as the night sky
Snakey's claws are as sharp as a deadly knife
Then his feet are so stinky like a rotten banana
Snakey is as vicious as a white tiger
Then Snakey's head is as round as the sun
Also, his toenails are as sharp as a dragon's claw
Afterwards, Snakey is a gelatin monster
And he helps me with me.

Tyler Bowyer (8)
Regis Manor Primary School, Milton Regis

All About Mega Max

Mega Max is crazy and destructive sometimes
But is also very good
Mega Max is also very bad
Mega Max is the only monster in the world
Mega Max likes to explore lots of different places
Mega Max likes to be the only monster in the wold
Mega Max is fun to play with
Mega Max is very, very playful
Mega Max is very funny
Mega Max is cool because he comes everywhere with me
Because it is very fun
Mega Max is crazy because he wrecks the house
Because he is sometimes very naughty

Mega Max is big because he is a monster
Mega Max is very loud
Mega Max is only sometimes annoying.

Robert Daniel Holmes (8)
Regis Manor Primary School, Milton Regis

Miku The Pink Monster

Mike has fluttering wings
And her body is bright pink
Her spots are blue like the ocean
With her mouth is an amazing emotion
Mike's beautiful wing can make a zap
But she cannot rap
Mike has sparkly green eyes
That are always open wide
She is smart and small
And she follows the monster school rules

Her body is round
But Mike's voice is not loud
She has huge, sharp wings
And she can blink
Mike's wings can make a giant sound
But she has flower petals from the ground.

Rusne Erichova (7)
Regis Manor Primary School, Milton Regis

Poem From Scareville About Mr Gobblechops

Mr Gobblechops is mischievous
Sometimes very pretentious
Mr Gobblechops loves kittens
He also has mittens
Lollies he loves
Also gummy gloves
He loves to scare
It is very rare

He is always hungry
Especially eating curry
Mr Gobblechops is scared
He gets glared
His friend lives in Surrey
But no time to talk, hurry
He's a monster
Also a romper
Mr Gobblechops is as hungry as can be.

Erin Victoria Brown (7)
Regis Manor Primary School, Milton Regis

All About Spike

Spike is funny
He likes to do lots of funny things
He also likes to do crazy things
Spike has lots of spikes on his back
That's why his name is Spike
Spike's eyes are terrible
Spike's tongue is green
Because he doesn't brush his tongue

Spike likes to eat some smelly children
And some smelly fish
He likes to dance around his kitchen
Spike smells because he doesn't have a bath.

Irene Ojo-Igbinoba (7)
Regis Manor Primary School, Milton Regis

Flob The Dog Monster

Flob is a dog
He is as crazy as pie
People call the dog Doge
I don't know why
He jumps in the air
As big as a spider
Flob is a dog monster

Leap and lap
His tail swishes
Cheeky little monster
Go! Go! Go!
Bark! Bark!
Let's celebrate Flob the monster
We celebrate today all over the world
Clever as ever
My dog monster
Hahaha! *Bark!*

Autumn Stone (8)
Regis Manor Primary School, Milton Regis

Cookie Fluff The Cute

Cookie Fluff has purple spikes all over his back
And it's like a hard log
He's fluffy and furry like a baby cat and dog
Cookie Fluff is a sweet-eater
He's as clumsy as a clown and scary
Cookie Fluff has a cute fox tail
He's big, shouty and fat
And he has black spots all over him
He is a furry little monster as well.

Roseanna Heron (7)
Regis Manor Primary School, Milton Regis

About The Destroyer

The Destroyer is so brave and strong
He is as fluffy as a rabbit
He is as big as 100cm
The Destroyer is scary like a tiger

He is as brave as a lion
The Destroyer is so scary
Every time someone comes
He stomps and he's thorny
He has such sharp claws
He can climb buildings.

Deivids Valdmanis (7)
Regis Manor Primary School, Milton Regis

Onserpancake The Monster

Onserpancake is a very silly and goofy monster
He is a towering and playful monster too
His lips do this noise when he eats: *crunch!*
Onserpancake is as playful as a bunny

Onserpancake is as silly as a clown
He is playful and jiggly too
His eyes are big like an elephant.

Ellie Telfer (7)
Regis Manor Primary School, Milton Regis

The Life Of Mr Stretchy

Mr Stretchy is a thin, kind monster
He always walks like a fierce tiger
His head is chubby and puffy and his legs are long

Mr Stretchy's arms are large
Also, his eyes are big
His eyes are on his ears
You have never seen an enchanted, special
monster like Mr Stretchy.

Jack Hancock (8)
Regis Manor Primary School, Milton Regis

Max The Hero

Max is a smart hero
He is the strongest in the whole world
His symbol is like a diamond
He has an E inside his diamond symbol
His enemy monster is Jack the Villain
Max and Jack fight. *Kapow! Boom!*
Max is as strong as all Avengers
Jack is as strong as Iron Man.

Madison Yuze Xue (7)
Regis Manor Primary School, Milton Regis

Thea The Savage

Thea is a nice monster,
When she is scared
She goes *kapow!* and *hiss!*
She likes cheese and chocolate
Also games

She can fly like a dragon
She also has a lot of eyes and arms
She's also tall
She is as good as a king.

Maximus Tyler Drake Goodman (7)
Regis Manor Primary School, Milton Regis

Bendy Monster

He bangs louder than a volcano
He loves to hug like marshmallows
He likes to sleep
He also likes bad jokes like the Annoying Orange
He is strong like grapefruit
He gets annoyed
He loves to read books.

Finley Sean Hooker (7)
Regis Manor Primary School, Milton Regis

Stinkary

Stinkary has three horrible eyes
He is wonderfully hairy
His tongue is as black as coal
And his teeth are scary
Hairy hands like enormous rocks
He smells like rotten cheese
And smelly socks!

Hayden John Pride (7), Kayden Barnes (7), Jai, Victor & Frankie
Regis Manor Primary School, Milton Regis

Mr Boby Fun

Mr Boby is hilarious and fun
He is sometimes called Happy
Mr Boby is big
Mr Boby is like jelly
Mr Boby is like a cuddly doll
Mr Boby is a fish
Mr Boby is less than one year old.

Ebony Rae Wood (7)
Regis Manor Primary School, Milton Regis

Blod

Blod likes food
Blod is scary
Blod loves scaring
Blod is as hungry as an alien

He is naughty
He has lots of friends
He is a serpent
He is fast.

Dylan Dooley (7)
Regis Manor Primary School, Milton Regis

Gary The Monster

Gary is clumsy
He is fine
He has five eyes
He is kind as a little puppy

Gary is wide
He does chores
He eats some chicken
His hat is silly.

Holly Macey (7)
Regis Manor Primary School, Milton Regis

Lizzy The Monster

Lizzy is as mischievous as can be
Lizzy is as big as Big Ben
Lizzy eats worms
She lives alone
Lizzy gets grumpy
When she is hungry.

Ruby Milburn (7)
Regis Manor Primary School, Milton Regis

Mike

He is revolting
He is vicious
He is serious
Mike's best friend is Sully
He has big horns.

Max Shrubsall (8)
Regis Manor Primary School, Milton Regis

YoungWriters®
— Est. 1991 —

YOUNG WRITERS INFORMATION

We hope you have enjoyed reading this book – and that you will continue to in the coming years.

If you're a young writer who enjoys reading and creative writing, or the parent of an enthusiastic poet or story writer, do visit our website **www.youngwriters.co.uk**. Here you will find free competitions, workshops and games, as well as recommended reads, a poetry glossary and our blog. There's lots to keep budding writers motivated to write!

If you would like to order further copies of this book, or any of our other titles, then please give us a call or order via your online account.

Young Writers
Remus House
Coltsfoot Drive
Peterborough
PE2 9BF
(01733) 890066
info@youngwriters.co.uk

Join in the conversation!
Tips, news, giveaways and much more!

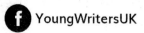 YoungWritersUK    @YoungWritersCW